Edition Schott

es

Carl Czerny
1791 – 1857

Vorschule der Geläufigkeit
Preliminary School of Velocity
30 Etudes de Mécanisme

für Klavier
for Piano

opus 849

Herausgegeben von / Edited by / Edité par
Wilhelm Ohmen

ED 9822
ISMN 979-0-001-13814-7

www.schott-music.com

Mainz · London · Berlin · Madrid · New York · Paris · Prague · Tokyo · Toronto
© 2006 SCHOTT MUSIC GmbH & Co. KG, Mainz · Printed in Germany

Inhalt / Contents / Contenu

Vorwort

Carl Czerny wurde am 20. Februar 1791 in Wien als Sohn des geschätzten Klavierlehrers Wenzel Czerny geboren. Seine Heimatstadt verließ er nur selten und starb dort am 15. Juli 1857. Unterrichtet und geprägt von seinem Vater begann er schon im Alter von drei Jahren Klavier zu spielen und wurde, dank seiner hohen Begabung, aber auch seines großen Fleißes wegen, als Neunjähriger Schüler Ludwig van Beethovens. Dessen Werke spielte er öffentlich und gab sie später heraus. Für Generationen von Pianisten geben diese Ausgaben, seine überlieferten Erläuterungen, vor allem auch seine Schrift *Über den richtigen Vortrag der sämtlichen Beethoven'schen Klavierwerke* (Universal Edition Wien, UE 13340) wichtige Hinweise und Anregungen für deren Interpretation.

Czerny war ein leidenschaftlicher Komponist. Er hinterlies mehr als eintausend Werke. Neben seinen Etüdensammlungen, bei denen eine Opuszahl oft aus fünfzig oder mehr Stücken besteht, komponierte er Messen, Opern, Orchester-, Klavier- und kammermusikalische Werke in sensiblem frühromantischen Stil. Igor Strawinsky spricht vom *blutvollen Musiker Czerny,* den er noch *höher schätze als den bedeutenden Pädagogen.* Czerny war schon in jungen Jahren ein anerkannter und sehr gefragter Klavierpädagoge. Zahlreiche Klavierschüler und Pianisten bildete er aus, darunter auch Franz Liszt.

Bedeutend und unübersehbar aber sind sein Etüdenwerk und seine klaviermethodischen Schriften. Sein Ziel war es, alle möglichen, damals bekannten spieltechnischen Figuren und Bewegungsabläufe grundlegend darzustellen und für den Unterricht einzurichten. Seine Sammlungen reichen von den ersten Fingerübungen und Studien für den Anfänger bis hin zu ausgedehnten Etüden höchsten Schwierigkeitsgrades. *Fleiß und Übung sind die einzigen Garanten zum Erfolg* – so Czerny. Er fordert aber auch die sensible, einfühlsame musikalische Interpretation, die *Schönheit des Vortrags und Gefühls,* welche dem einfachen *Gesange* zukommen.

Der vorliegende Band „Vorschule der Geläufigkeit" ist für den etwas fortgeschrittenen Klavierspieler gedacht. Die Stücke sind ungefähr in aufsteigender Schwierigkeit angeordnet. Verschiedene elementare, grundlegende Techniken sollen zu einer ersten pianistischen Geläufigkeit und Flexibilität führen:
Übung im Fünftonraum (Nr. 1), Phrasierung (Nr. 2), Triolen (Nr. 3, 20), gehaltene Melodietöne (Nr. 4), scharfe Punktierung (Nr. 5), Dynamik (Nr. 6), Albertische Bässe – Begleitfiguren - (Nr. 7), schnelle Tonleitern (Nr. 8, 9,10,14,18,29), kleinere Intervalle im Wechsel der Hände (Nr. 10), Repetitionen (Nr. 12, 26), Leggiero (Nr. 13), Arpeggien (Nr. 15, 25), Stärkung der Finger (Nr. 16), Pralltriller und Vorschläge (Nr. 17), Chromatik (Nr. 21), Trillervorübung (Nr. 22), versetzte, synkopische Aufeinanderfolge (Nr. 24), Übergreifen der Hände (Nr. 27), Repetitionen von Dreiklängen (Nr. 28), Unisono-Tonleitern (Nr. 18, 30).

Die Metronomzahlen und Fingersätze stammen vom Herausgeber. Sie sind der Spielart auf heutigen Klavieren mit moderner Mechanik angepasst, denn die Instrumente der damaligen Zeit mit Wiener Mechanik hatten einen leichteren Anschlag, eine engere Oktavspanne und kürzere Vordertasten. Fingersätze in Klammern können alternativ angewendet werden; sie ermöglichen teilweise eine bequemere Ausführung. Alle Übungen sollen langsam einstudiert und im Tempo gesteigert werden. Auch bei Nichterreichen des vorgeschlagenen Zeitmaßes werden sie von Nutzen sein. Diese Stücke sind vor allem als Vorübungen für die Bewältigung der leichten bis mittelschweren Klavierliteratur sehr hilfreich.

Wilhelm Ohmen

Preface

Carl Czerny was born in Vienna on 20 February 1791 and lived there until his death on 15 July 1857, rarely leaving the city of his birth. His father was the respected piano teacher Wenzel Czerny, under whose instruction and influence Carl started playing the piano at the age of three; thanks to the boy's remarkable gifts and hard work, Ludwig van Beethoven took him on as a pupil when he was only nine. Carl Czerny performed Beethoven's works in public and later published them: these editions with their accompanying explanations, and in particular Czerny's writings *On the correct way to perform all Beethoven's piano works* (Universal Edition Vienna, UE 13340) have been a source of essential advice and inspiration for generations of pianists.

Czerny was a prolific composer who left behind him more than a thousand works. Besides his collections of studies, where a single opus number often represents fifty or more pieces, he composed masses, operas, orchestral, piano and chamber music works in the early Romantic style. Igor Stravinsky speaks of *Czerny the red-blooded musician,* whom he rated even *higher than as an influential teacher.* Even as a young man, Czerny was recognised and much in demand as a piano teacher. He taught many pupils and trained a number of pianists, including Franz Liszt.

His major legacy, however, is the studies and tutorial works he wrote for the piano. It was Czerny's aim to give an outline presentation of all the figures and patterns of notes that pianists in his day were likely to encounter and to arrange them for tuition purposes. His collections of studies range from initial finger exercises for beginners to extensive and extremely difficult studies. *Hard work and plenty of practice are the only reliable paths to success,* according to Czerny. He also called for sensitive musical interpretation, though: the *beauty of playing and the sensitivity that approaches the simplicity of song.*

Preliminary exercises in articulation

This volume of "Preliminary exercises in articulation" is intended for the moderately advanced pianist. The pieces are presented in approximate order of increasing difficulty. Mastering a range of elementary, fundamental techniques should equip the pianist with basic articulation skills and flexibility:
Five-finger exercise (No. 1), phrasing (No. 2), triplets (Nos. 3 & 20), legato melodies (No. 4), clear *staccato* playing (No. 5), dynamics (No. 6), *Alberti* bass accompaniments (No. 7), rapid scales (Nos. 8, 9, 10, 14, 18, 29), smaller intervals with alternating hands (No. 10), repeated notes (Nos. 12 & 26), *leggiero* playing (No. 13), arpeggios (Nos. 15 & 25), strengthening the fingers (No. 16), playing trills and grace notes (No. 17), chromatic passages (No. 21), preliminary exercise for playing trills (No. 22), staggered and syncopated sequences (No. 24), crossing over the hands (No. 27), repetition of chords (No. 28), unison scales (Nos. 18 & 30).

Metronome figures and fingerings are by the editor. These are designed to suit playing on modern pianos and their mechanism – the Viennese instruments of Czerny's day had a lighter touch, a narrower octave span and shorter white keys. Fingerings in brackets may be used as alternatives; some of them may be found more comfortable. All the exercises should be played slowly at first, then at gradually increased speed. Even if the suggested tempo is never achieved, they will still be useful. These pieces should be particularly helpful as preliminary exercises for mastering easy to moderately difficult works in the piano repertoire.

Wilhelm Ohmen
English translation Julia Rushworth

Etudes de Mécanisme

Vorschule zur „Schule der Geläufigkeit" opus 849

Carl Czerny
1791 - 1857

51 675

7

2

Vivace giocoso ♩ = 76

5

51 675

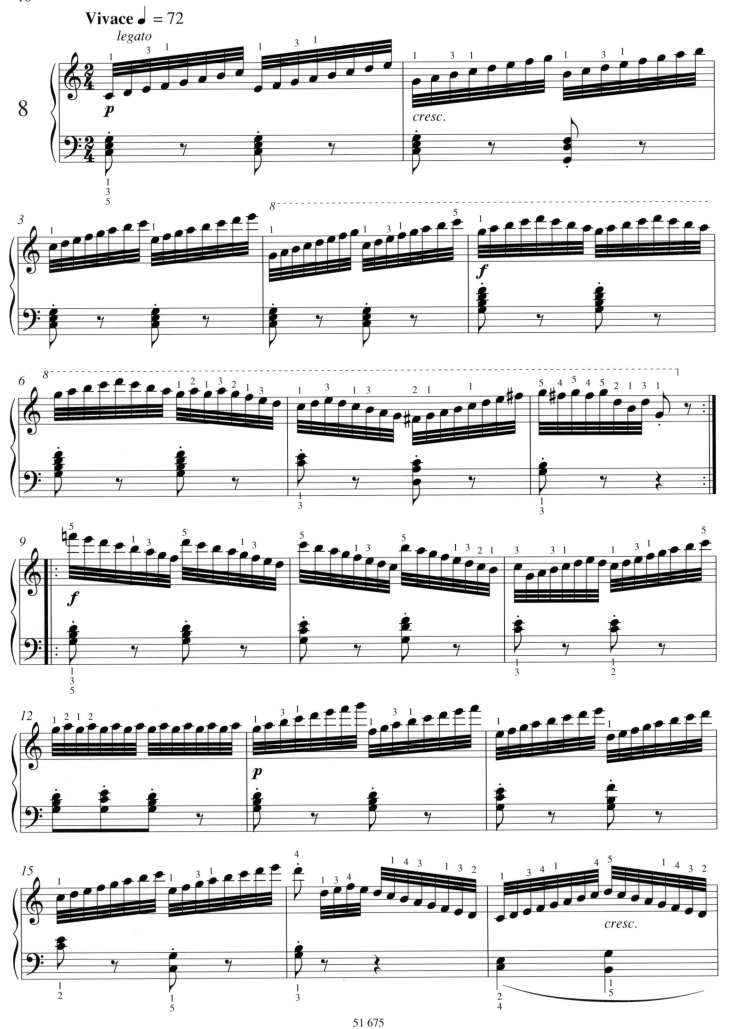

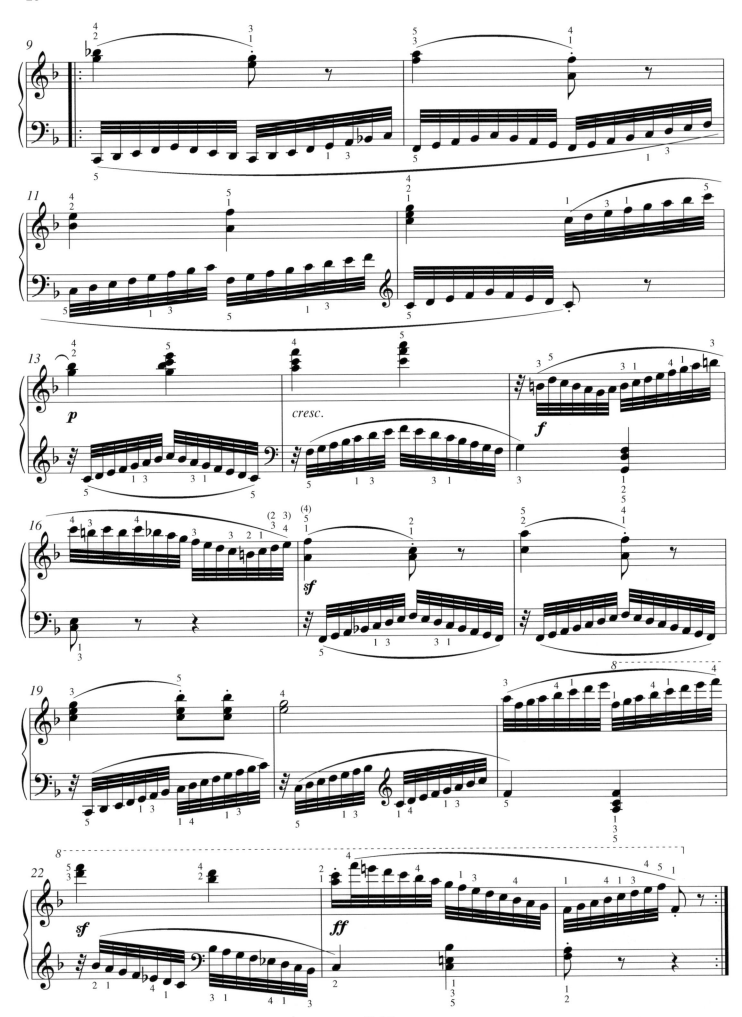

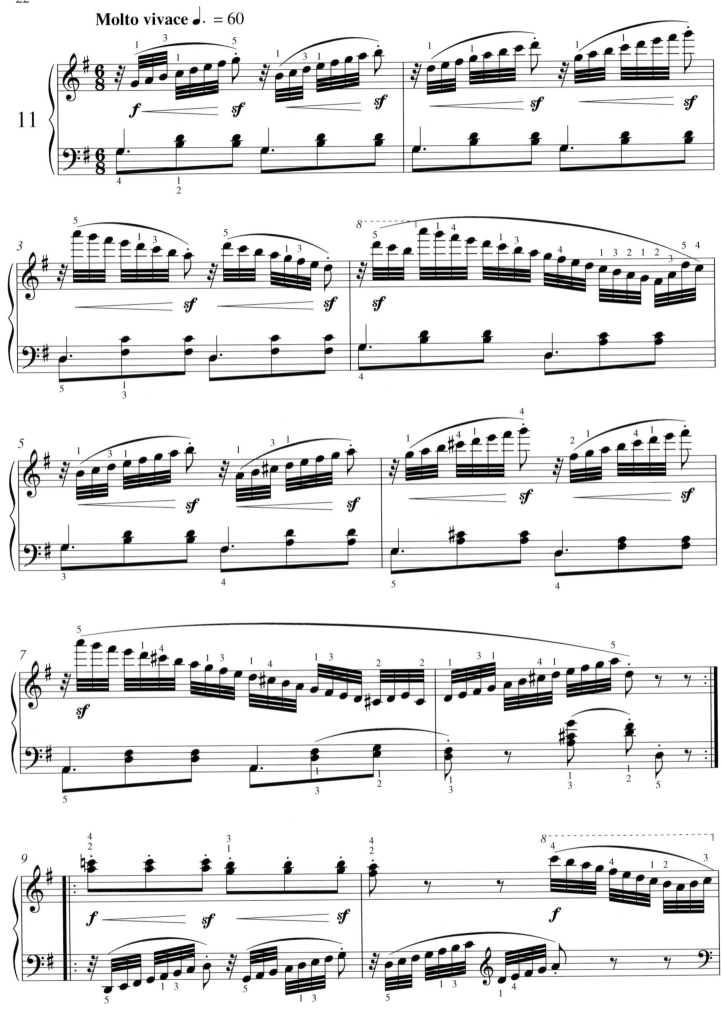

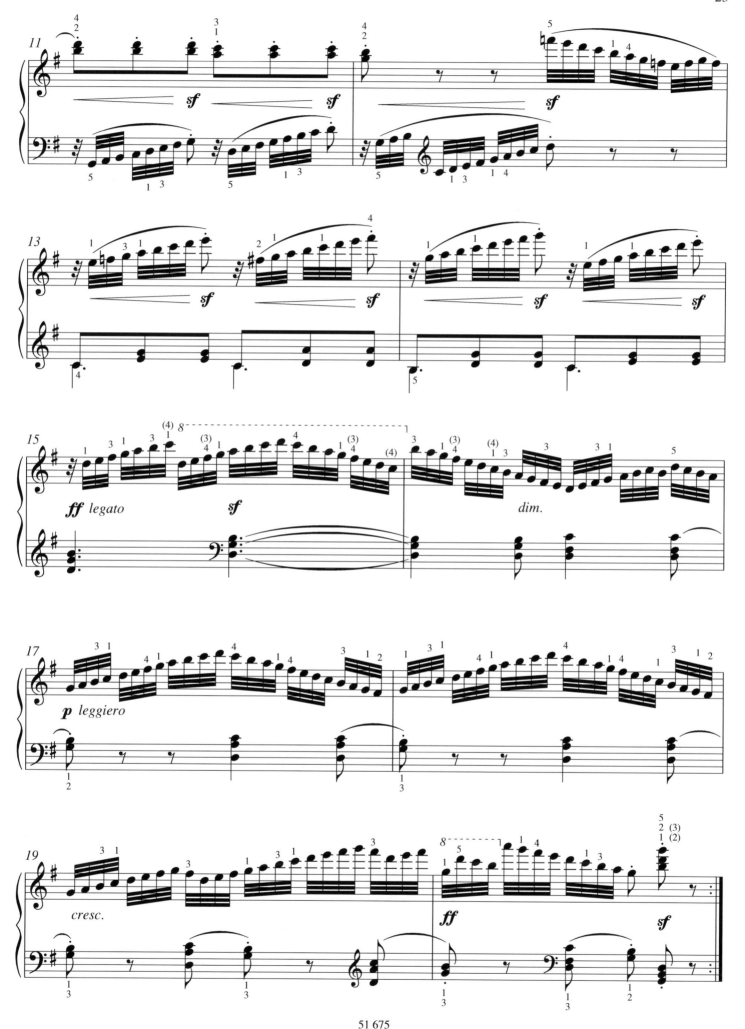

51 675

Molto vivace e leggiero ♩. = 88

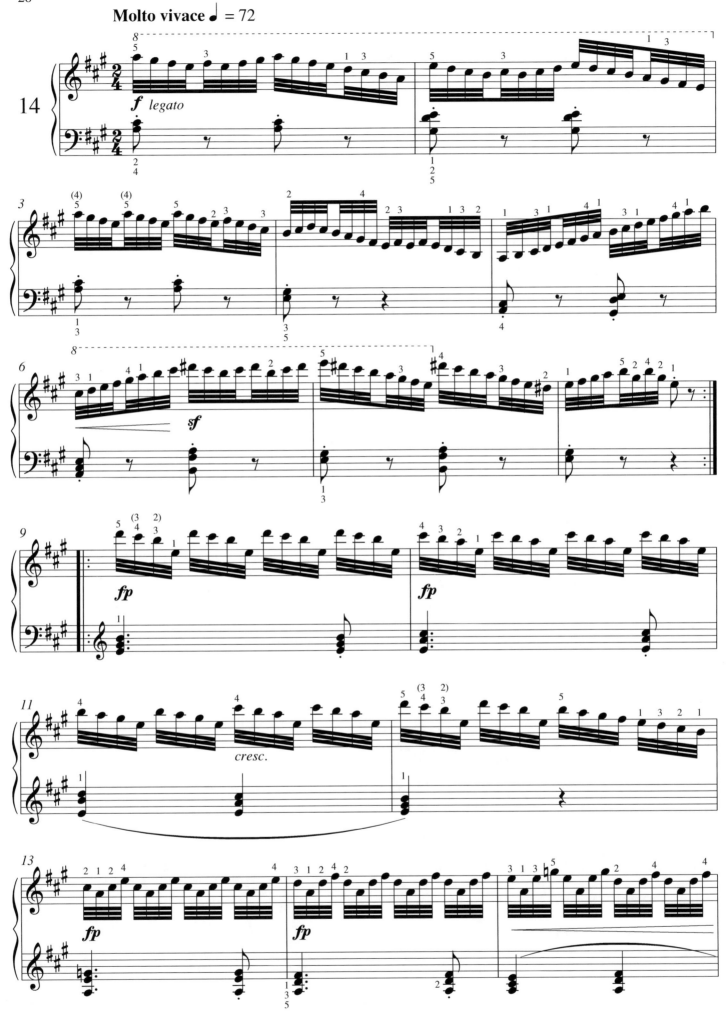

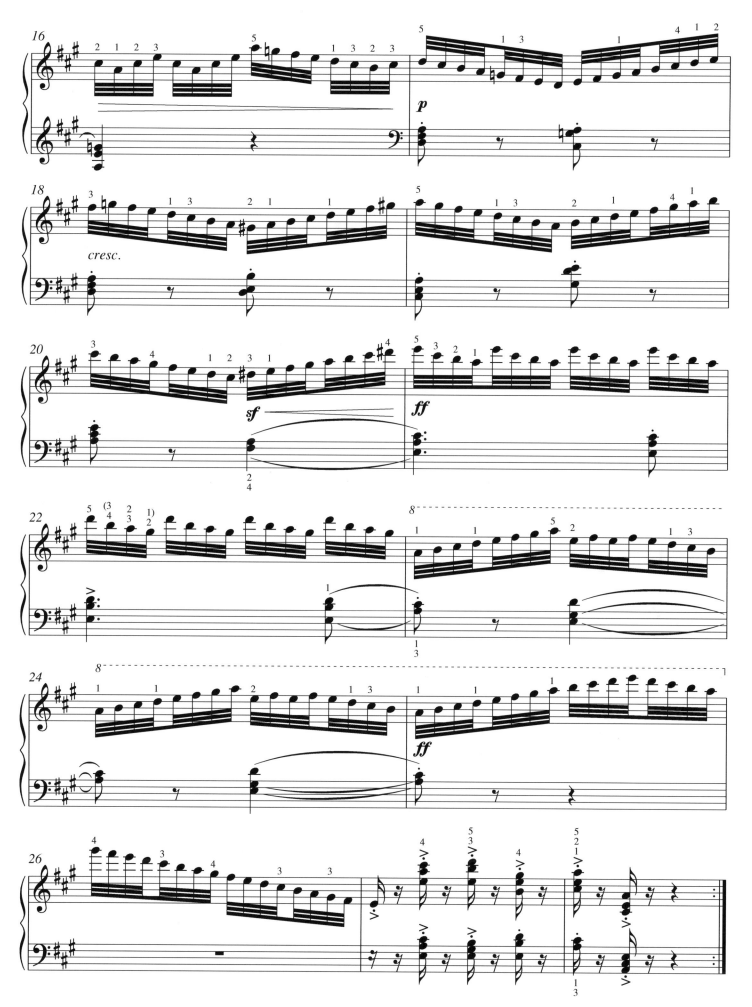

Allegretto vivace ♩ = 66

15

51 675

Molto vivace energico ♩ = 84

16

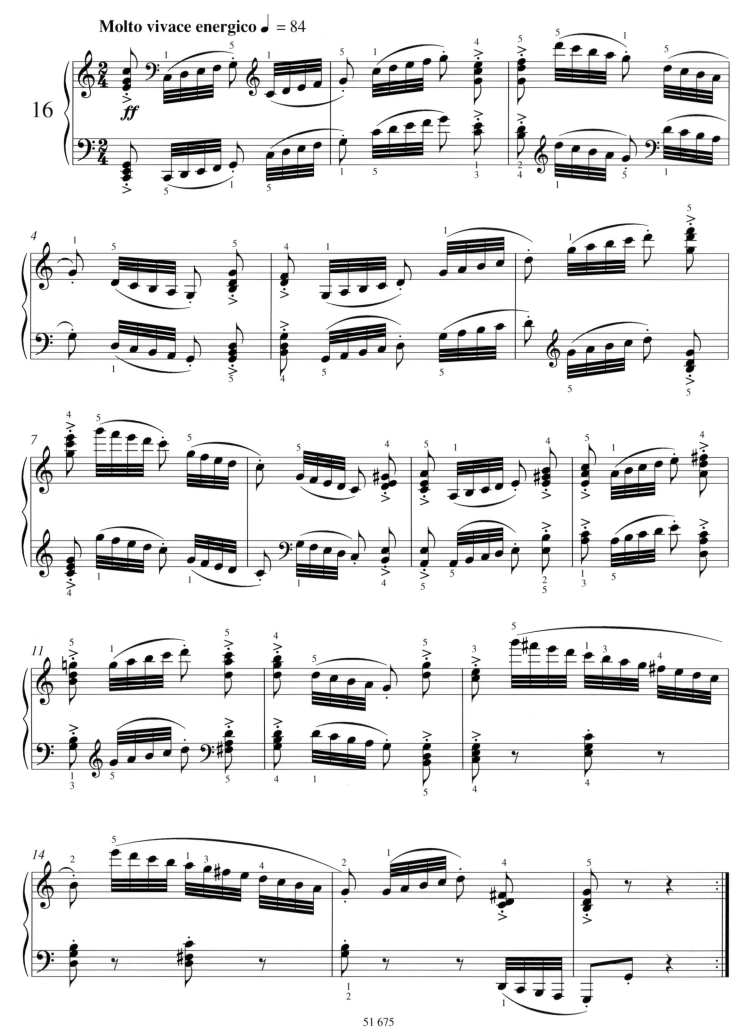

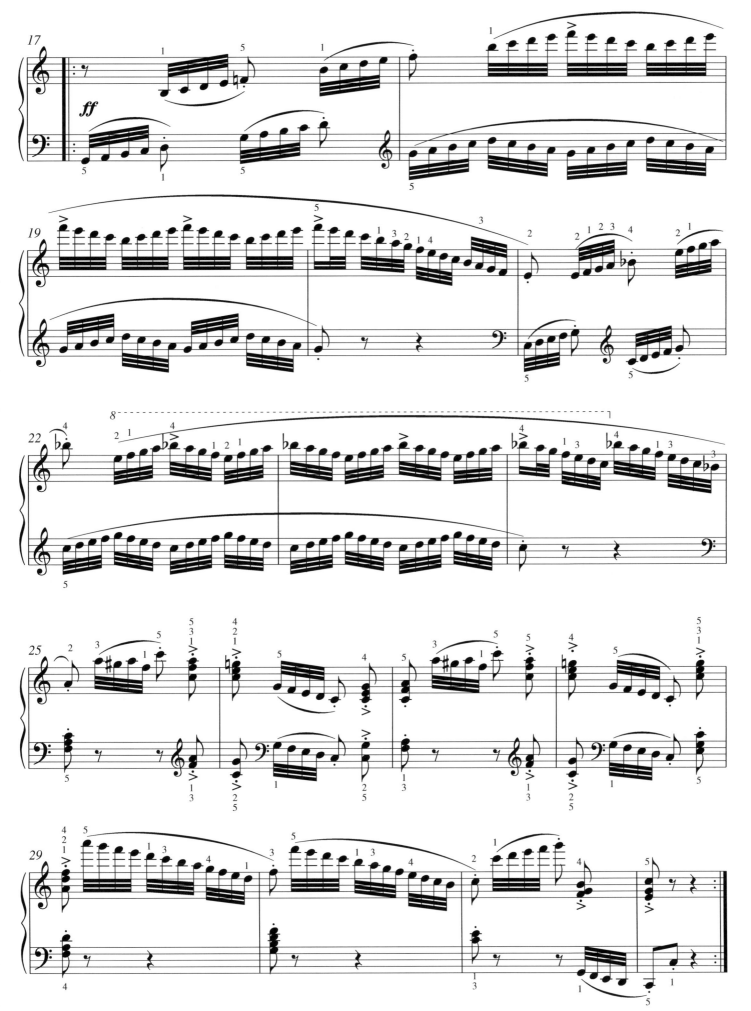

Vivace giocoso ♩ = 96

17

Allegro vivo ♩ = 138

21

legato

pp *delicamente veloce*

Allegro comodo ♩ = 112

27

Allegro molto ♩ = 160

29

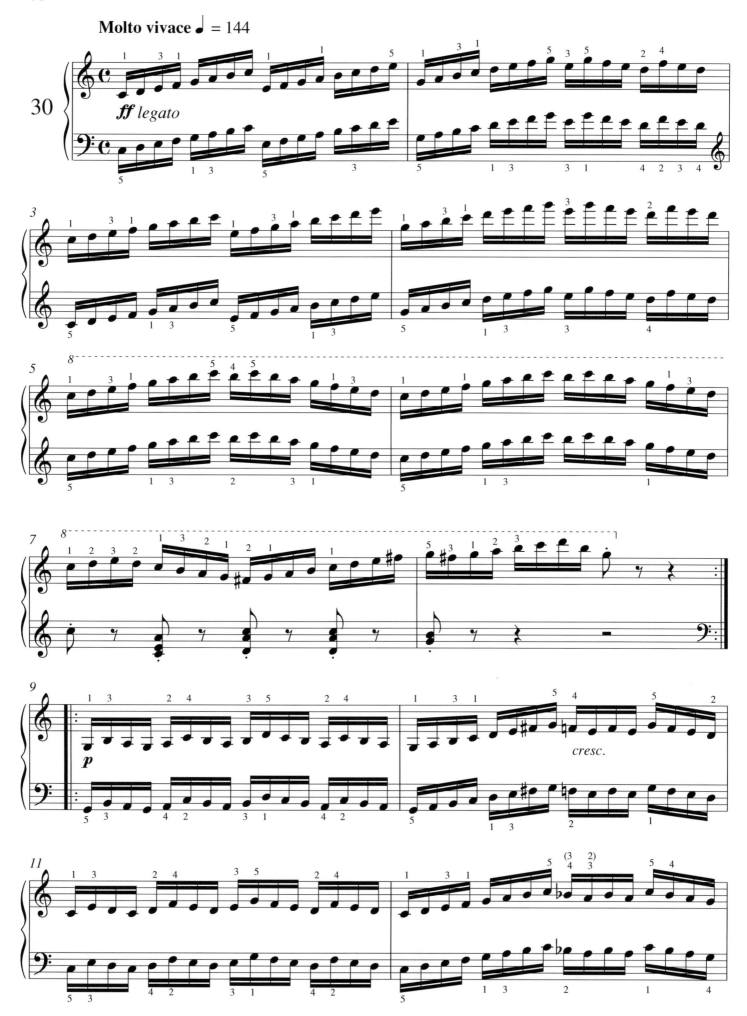

Schott Music, Mainz 51 675